Mrs Large

Mrs Large is always in a rush as she struggles to cope with her four children and mountains of washing. But she always has time to join in the fun!

Laura Large

Helpful and good-natured, Laura is a caring big sister to baby Lucy. She is creative and practical and enjoys making things.

Lucy Large

Lucy is the baby of the family. She gets into mischief the moment Mrs Large turns her back and her naughty little trunk finds its way into everything.

First published 2009 by Walker Books Ltd
87 Vauxhall Walk, London SE11 5HJ

2 4 6 8 10 9 7 5 3 1

Copyright © 2009 Coolabi, Go-N Productions, Luxanimation & DQ Entertainment
Based on the animation series THE LARGE FAMILY by JILL MURPHY
Developed and produced by Coolabi and Go-N Productions (France)
in association with Luxanimation and DQ Entertainment

This book has been typeset in Bembo Educational.

Printed in China

British Library Cataloguing in Publication Data: a catalogue record for this book
is available from the British Library

ISBN 978-1-4063-1987-3

www.walker.co.uk

Grandpa in Trouble

Based on the Large Family stories by Jill Murphy

WALKER BOOKS

AND SUBSIDIARIES

LONDON · BOSTON · SYDNEY · AUCKLAND

It was mayhem at the breakfast table.
Lester and Luke were fighting over the toy
in the new box of cereal.
"It's *my* turn to have it!" Lester shouted.
"No, it's not!" argued Luke. "It's *mine!*"

The packet burst open and cereal flew
everywhere as Luke fell over backwards.
"RIGHT," said Mrs Large, "that's enough!"

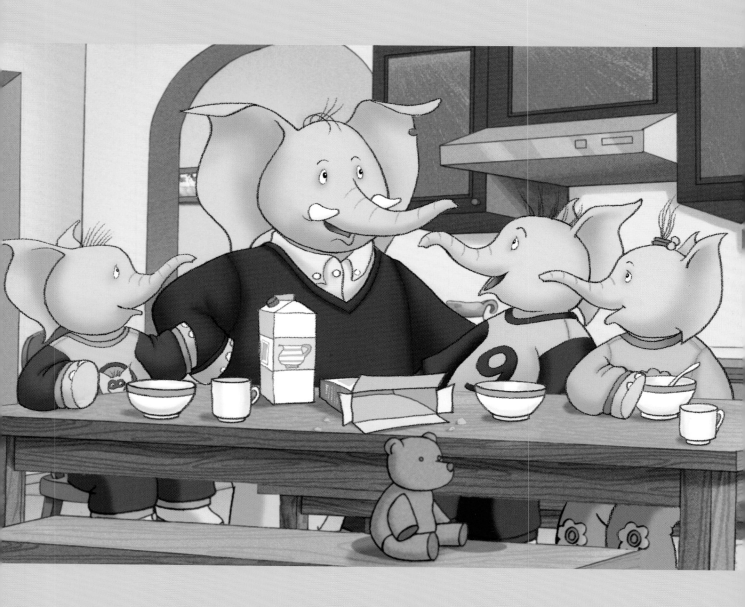

Mr Large came into the kitchen. "I'm taking you for a picnic in the countryside," he announced, with a smile.

"Hooray!" shouted the children.

"Not you lot," said Mr Large. "I meant just Mum and me."

"But there's no one to look after the children," said Mrs Large.

"Don't worry, dear," said Mr Large. "Granny and Grandpa are already on their way."

"Oh no!" cried Mrs Large in horror. "You might have warned me. The house is a tip!"

Everyone rushed around trying to get the house
cleared up before Granny and Grandpa arrived.
The children tidied their rooms and Mrs Large
did the hoovering while Mr Large packed the
picnic basket.

"Now, you must all behave yourselves," instructed Mrs Large, "and be helpful to Granny and Grandpa."

'Don't worry," Mr Large assured her, "the children will be as good as gold."

"Of course they will!" said Granny.

"Can we play football after lunch?"
asked Lester.

"Of course you can," replied Granny.
Grandpa reached for a sandwich and
knocked over his juice.

"Really, you're so clumsy," said Granny.

"I'm glad it wasn't us," whispered Laura.

Grandpa went out into the garden to play football with the children.

"Come on, Luke," he said proudly. "I'll show you how to score a goal."

CRASH! The ball smashed straight through the living-room window.

"Look at what you've done!" cried Granny.
"You naughty children!"
The children looked embarrassed.
"Actually," said Grandpa, "it wasn't the children. It was me."
"But it was a brilliant goal!" said Lester brightly.

"Grandpa was meant to be looking after the baby," said Granny crossly. "WHERE IS THE BABY?!"

Laura found Lucy in the garden, covered
in mud.
"Goodness me!" cried Granny. "You're
filthy! I'd better take you up for a bath.
That naughty grandpa."
"I'm glad it wasn't us," whispered Lester,
as Granny went upstairs to run a bath.

Meanwhile Grandpa tried to fix the bookcase, which had been broken by the football. But at the last moment, the shelf collapsed on top of him! Granny rushed downstairs.

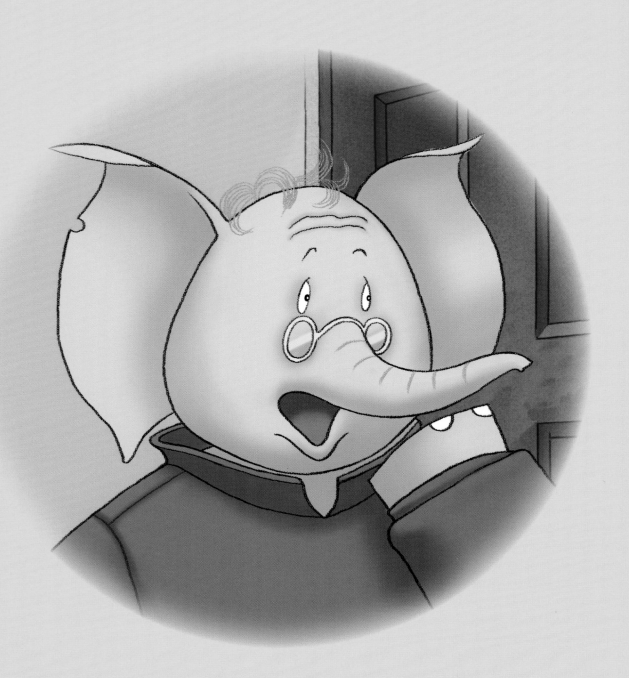

"*Now*, what are you doing?!" gasped Granny.
"You're wrecking the place!"

"Don't be cross, dear," groaned Grandpa. "I think I've done something awful to my trunk."

Granny, Grandpa and the children all set off to Dr Jolly's surgery.
"Poor Grandpa," said Laura. "I hope it's not too painful."

Meanwhile, out in the countryside, Mrs Large
was admiring the view.

"I've had such a lovely day," she said to
Mr Large. "I hope Granny and Grandpa are
coping all right."

"No need to worry," said Mr Large. "They're
brilliant with the kids. I'm sure everything is
under control."

While Grandpa saw the doctor, everyone
sat in the waiting room.
"Grandpa's been in there for ages," said
Laura. "I do hope he's all right."

At last, Grandpa and the doctor came out.
Lucy giggled when she saw the bandage
on Grandpa's trunk.

"I don't know what *you're* laughing at, young lady," said Dr Jolly. "You look as if you could do with a bath."

"OH NO!" exclaimed Granny. "THE BATH!"

Mr and Mrs Large arrived home. The first
thing they saw as they opened the front door
was water pouring down the stairs.
"The house is flooded!" cried Mrs Large.
"I think someone's left the bath tap running,"
replied Mr Large.

In the living room, things were even worse.
"Look at the mess in here!" said Mrs Large.
"What *has* been going on? Those *naughty*
children."

Just at that moment, Granny and Grandpa arrived back from the doctor's with all the children in tow.

"What *have* you been up to?" demanded Mrs Large. "We can't leave you for five minutes. You've really let us down!"

"But it wasn't us!" said Lester indignantly.

"It's true," said Granny, "it *wasn't* them. We did it. It was all *our* fault. We're ever so sorry."

Mr and Mrs Large looked at each other in astonishment.

"Don't worry," said Grandpa, "we'll clear it all up."

"They didn't do it on purpose," said Luke. "They were just accidents."

Later, after the grandparents had gone home,
Mrs Large told everyone how much she had
enjoyed her day out with Daddy.
"I told you the children would be as good
as gold," said Mr Large.
"I just wish we could say the same for their
grandparents!" laughed Mrs Large.

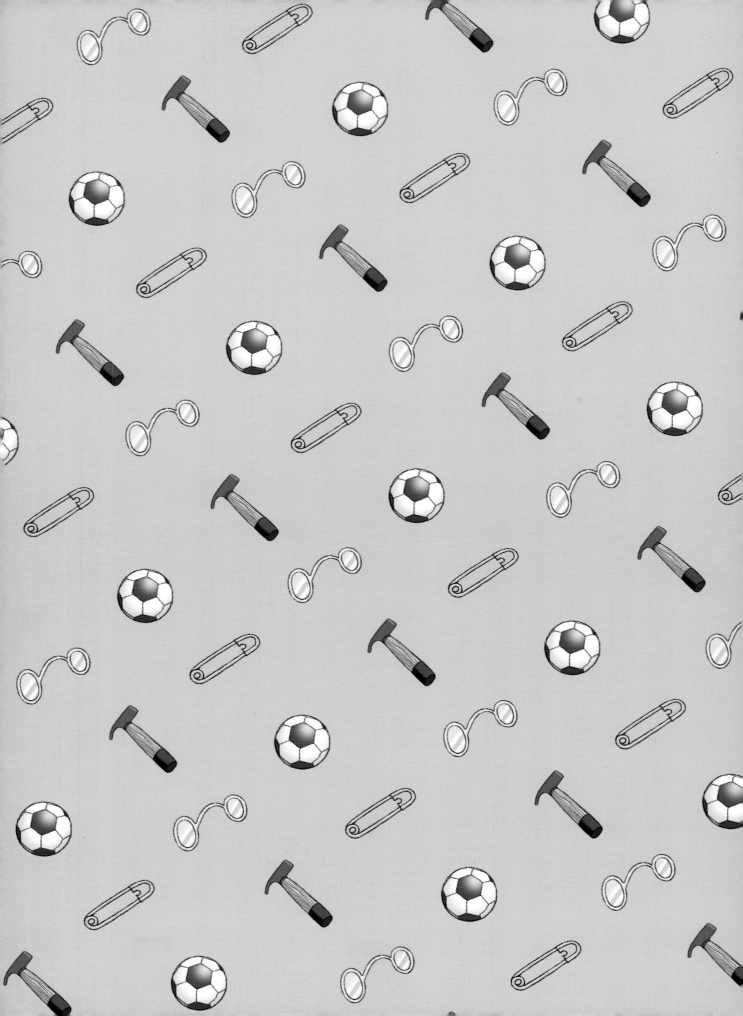

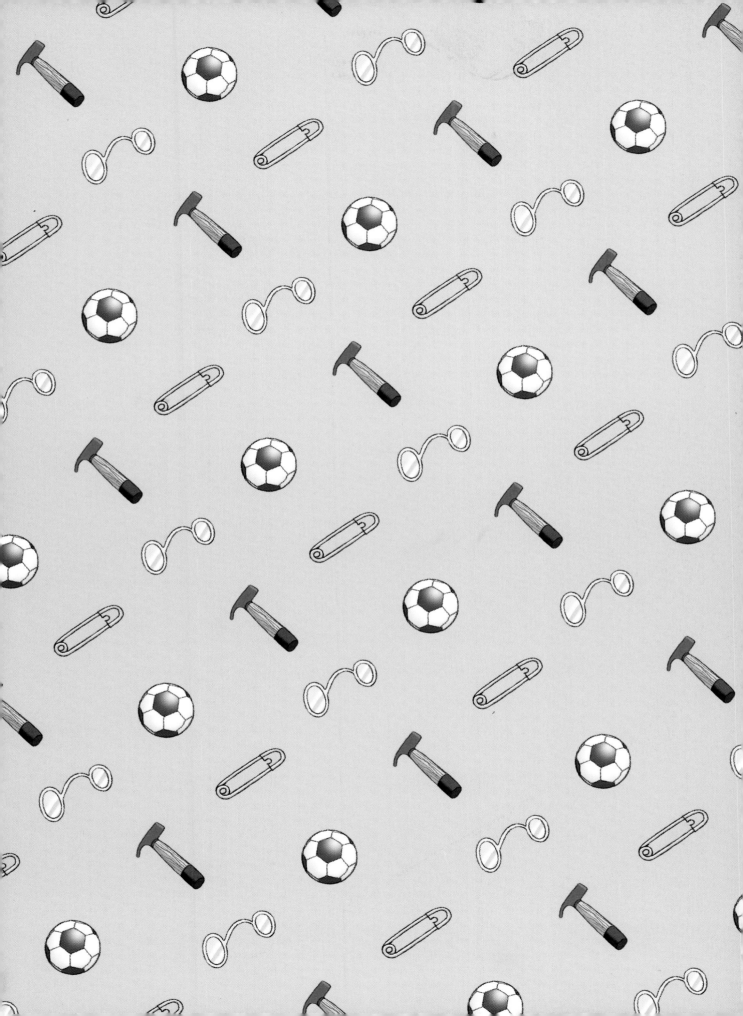

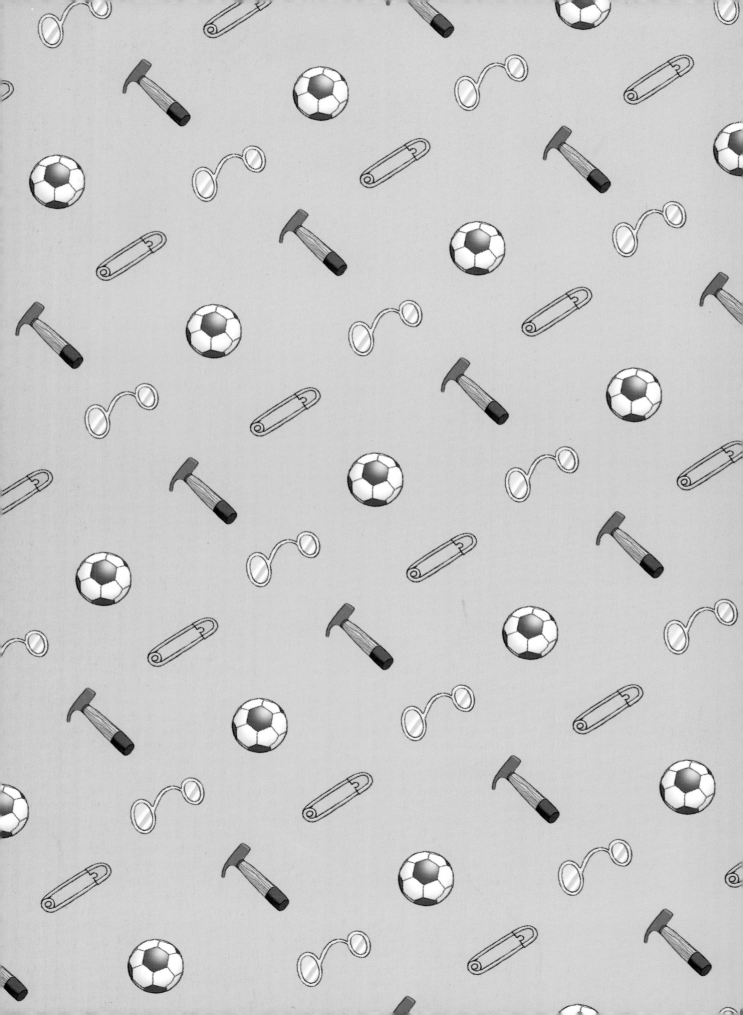